Published and Distributed in the United States By:

Natural Advantage
69-1010 Keana Pl., C-101
Kamuela, HI 96743

1-800-293-2911

Edited By: Beth McCormick
Final Editor: Barbara Bates
Designed By: Shannon Anderson

Library Of Congress Catalog Card No.: 96-72168

Grunden, Tom

Celebration of Silence/ Tom Grunden

ISBN-0-9655885-0-5 (Trade Paper)
1. Health   2. Meditation

ISBN-0-9655885-0-5
First Printing, January 1997
Printed in the United States of America

If unavailable in local bookstores, additional copies of this book, audio cassette programs and videos may be purchased by writing the publisher at the above address or by calling:
1-800-293-2911.

Celebration of Silence

by
Tom Grunden

Natural Advantage

Dedication

I would like to dedicate this book to all who have ever felt that deep longing for something more than is normally offered in this world. To those who have nurtured this discontent until it becomes a force that changes the very fabric of their lives.

I would also like to dedicate this book to everyone who has been ill and felt helpless at their loss of health. To those for whom helplessness has become a burden, I offer my hand. If feeling helpless has spurred you toward a deeper understanding of strength, I offer my encouragement to continue the search. The source of that strength is near.

A special dedication goes out to that portion of all our lives that others refer to as old age. May our gaze not become fixed on society's exaltation of youth and fear of death. But, rather, may we embrace this opportunity for expansion so that our potential matures. This creates the dignity we all deserve.

Acknowledgements

In the writing of this book I had the help and support of four wonderful women. Although the idea for the book had been floating around for some time (my Aunt Dorothy tried to get me to send her my stories in the late '70s), it was not until Kathy Mason began attending my classes and eventually took on the catalytic role of producer, that everything began to fall into place. Thank you Kathy for your faith in me and all our projects.

A special thanks goes to Beth McCormick for listening to my stories for more than three years, so that they became almost a part of her. She was then willing to stop writing her own book in order to edit this one. Thank you for the love and enthusiasm that you brought to this writing.

I would also like to thank Barbara Bates for her calming influence as final editor. Your professionalism and heart coexist in such a wonderful harmony.

Last, and most important, I want to thank Gandha for the most beautiful thirteen years I have ever had. I love you Gandha. Your support and flexibility has made this book a joy.

Death is an interesting phenomenon. It is in the works for all of us at a certain point in time and the very idea holds a lot of fascination to us.

Death is a myth that we have simply misunderstood. This misunderstanding makes death appear real, and creates fear and apprehension.

We think of ourselves at the center of our world, and what is really at the center is silence. If we come to terms with that centering of silence, then death disappears as a problem. As long as the self is at the center, death is a reality. As soon as silence becomes the center, death disappears, it doesn't exist anymore. These two are tied very intimately together.

The whole near-death experience, and living with it all these years, has shown me that when death comes it strips away all that is nonessential. Everything that's not at the very essence disappears. Our body disappears, our mind as we know it disappears, our relationships, our life, all our basic reality is altered. But something doesn't change. If we become familiar with that inner truth, that core of silence, then death itself disappears.

To know this truth while we live, reveals the tremendous opportunity that is our life. The opportunity to live without fear, to allow love to penetrate every aspect of our world, to allow light to pour through us, and to continually experience that up-welling of gratitude that is the glory of being human.

Now I will tell you my story...

One

A faint buzz stirred the desert air, where for two days there had been only the sound of the wind and the crunch of my own footsteps. Pausing midstride, I listened.

The rock outcropping ahead cast a little bit of shade, a rest spot where I dropped my pack, and allowed myself a sip from the canteen. The buzzing sound grew closer, and soon a bee landed not thirty feet away, then another.

Beckoning me, the bees danced their zigzag pattern in the general southwesterly direction I'd been heading. This was the most certainty I'd felt in the three months I'd been planning this crazy excursion.

Bees in the desert could only mean one thing...surface water, an oasis. In the next hour's hike, I must have seen dozens of bees, and soon I could smell, and even hear the water.

To the end of my days I'll never forget the moment I climbed over the rocks and caught my first sight of that sacred place, a waterfall in the midst of all this desert. Like some miraculous crystal pillar it stood, water rushing gloriously from a small upper pool, down an eight foot drop, into a larger, shallow pool, where the stream again went underground. Ferns grew between the damp rocks, a luxurious green, unlike any plant for miles. I paused, absolutely still for perhaps an hour.

I remembered exactly why I always came into the wilderness. The silence. The sounds. The sounds never disturbed the silence, but gave it a voice.

Soon, shedding my clothes, I waded into the water, letting the torrent stream all over me, washing away the city, washing away my thoughts, washing away the dust of three days travel.

After I had my initial cleansing in that sweet water, I backed away with my tent and pack, knowing that animals came to this place as well. I found an area above to set up camp, well out of the way of any flash floods that can happen so suddenly in the desert. It was close enough to hear the water moving, to feel the animals when they came to the water, but not so close to keep them from coming.

The next few days were filled with exploration, with immersing myself again and again in the pools. The heat of the afternoon was spent stretched out on the damp rock behind the curtain of falling water. The tensions in my body were pummeled gently away by the motion of cascading water.

Often, I would read the I Ching. A real luxury in a pack that had to contain so much water and food, this book was a constant companion, a nature based system of thought from an ancient time and place, so relevant to my own time in the wilderness.

I quietly observed the animals who drank from this oasis, the rabbits, hawks and coyotes, as well as the lizards and snakes who lived among the rocks and cacti. I never felt the desire to hunt here, and the animals became accustomed to my discreet presence. I knew there was food to supplant what I brought, the tubers that grew underground, the hearts of certain edible cactus, and the delicate fern shoots that grew by the stream.

As the days went by I felt the frustration arise within me. By the fourth day of solitude, I knew a restlessness would well up inside. My life in the world, relationships, situations, activities, all of the dust and turmoil of life would arise, leaving me feeling edgy and not quite comfortable in my own skin.

I knew enough to welcome that frustration, because once it passed, there would be no difference between the stillness of the desert and the stillness within me. On those days I would be particularly attentive, because the more quietly alert I was, the more quickly it would move through.

By the fifth day, I felt no separation from the environment I was in...the waterfall, the desert, the color of the sky in the early mornings and the late after-noons, the animals, the heat that cleansed the land-scape every day, the moonlight that bathed it at night.

Then the days would begin to roll by much more quickly, sunrises and sunsets, one after another. Even that didn't feel like the passing of time. It felt like the joy of nature, expressing herself with color and origi-nality. The silence of those days melted into the si-lence within my heart, until each of my actions un-folded out of that blessed emptiness.

Any action done out of mind, out of thinking, done inappropriately, with distraction, stood out so clearly. But after two weeks, none of those abrupt actions occurred. Everything was an expression of silence, the breathing, the sleeping, the walking. Everything unfolded out of that wholeness.

This was a high contrast from the world of people, where everything seemed to be separate from every-thing else. Each person pulled and pushed in a differ-ent direction, with motivations hidden behind every action. Each activity seemed to impinge on existing activities, and everything demanded time, demanded space, demanded attention.

This world of people left me thirsty in a way that only the desert seemed to satisfy. Rarely did I see, in the depths of people's eyes, that they understood silence. Instead, they seemed to expend their energies on ceaseless activity. It was physically painful to be around such restless people, unaware of their own discontent, but very obviously dissatisfied. It was a constant reminder to me not to waste my time. I came to regard that thirst as very important. That thirst for the nourishment of the soul, for solitude and silence, was more important than all the details and circumstances of my life. Watching the people around me and experiencing their lives was a reminder to me of what was important, and it deepened my own thirst.

My love of maps led me to this desert. I used to cover my walls with maps, big and small, old maps, colorful maps, exotic maps. I particularly loved the Chihuahua Desert, straddling the border of Texas and Mexico, and I owned every map of it that could be had. I would study them for hours at a time.

The maps show the desert is full of dry ravines, where water runs only a few days out of every year. In some places there are streams that carry water from the mountains through these foothills, but the water is almost always underground. I would follow the little dotted blue lines marking these dry ravines and underground rivers, and at one point I saw that two of the tiny dots were joined together to form a very short blue line. The solid blue lines that marked surface water did not occur for many miles. At the time I knew it might be a printing error, an extra dot on a map that had so many dots already.

But over a period of several months I stared at this map, wondering, What if...? What if there's something there? What if this map's correct?

Somehow, looking at those dots for those many months, this expedition was conceived. So when I started, I knew that I was probably walking a helluva long way just to confirm a printing error. It had taken one day of driving to reach the point where I left the car and started out on foot. I carried enough water for three and a half days, in case there was nothing there and I had to return. All the time, I was hoping there was water, and miraculously, here it was. I was surrounded by it.

It was my father who introduced me to silence. I never thought about the way he was as being specifically Native American. After all, nobody was doing the ceremonial dances, talking about their heritage, or even thinking about it. But in a thousand subtle ways, that's what I was being taught the whole time I was growing up.

My father rarely spoke, but when he did, they were simple, practical words. But we spent many, many hours engaged with each other quite harmoniously.

As a very young child, I knew that if I could be as quiet and alert as he was, without his needing to silence me, and if I could keep up with the grown men without slowing them down or breaking their rhythm, I would soon take part in their hunts.

At first he would take my brother and me on practice hunts, an afternoon or an early morning's hike through the brush. Then, as we learned to step without sound and to intuit his direction without words, these stretched to day long, and occasional overnight ventures.

The annual hunts drew my uncles from 600 miles away, and were anticipated months in advance. My one uncle was slightly higher strung than my Dad, especially with kids. Compared to anyone else he's the most laid back person in the world, but we knew he'd give us trouble if we held them back for a minute.

They weren't really impatient with us, it was just that these hunts were serious endeavors. No allowances were made for children. If you weren't able to keep up, you simply were too young to go. It was not unusual for us to cover twenty five miles in one day, and I remember once we actually walked forty.

When my Dad was growing up, ammunition was valuable, not something to be wasted. My grandfather used to count out the bullets he gave to my Dad, and however many shots he took, that's how much game he was expected to bring home. For my Dad and uncles, that very intent, focused attitude about hunting never wavered.

The lessons I learned through hunting have rewarded me every day of my life. I learned to notice everything, to be aware of each person's mood, as well as my own thoughts and feelings. Out in the wilderness, if someone is even slightly preoccupied, the animals will hear them. The animals' senses are acute, undistracted by thoughts.

Among us, being centered was considered normal, and when someone was off center, it became painfully obvious. Not wanting to humiliate them by pointing it out, we waited for them to notice. Only if someone persisted in stepping on you, banging into you, would you say something, and even then you'd apologize, wanting to leave that person their dignity. If they still didn't notice, you might simply leave, which is a very strong statement. Trouble is, in this culture, even that is likely to go unnoticed.

One of my Dad's friends from work always wanted to go hunting with us. Although my Dad had some misgivings, somehow it happened that this guy, his friend, and his son went along. Those three just didn't know how to blend in. For one thing, they talked a lot. By other people's standards, they were quiet, but to us, they talked too much. They threw our rhythm completely off without even recognizing they were doing it. My Dad's silence changed color when he was displeased, and I was amazed to watch that happening without their noticing it. That's when I first realized other people were seeing the world in very different ways than we were.

We didn't like the way they handled their weapons, either. They were dangerous. They walked around with their guns off safety, moving over rough ground, thinking about everything but what they were doing.

They seemed likely to go shooting off in any direction, and that's when we called the hunt off. We all climbed back in the truck and rode home, those guys still unaware of anything amiss.

It was not until I was an adult that I realized how much Native blood I had. We lived in a normal subdivision, went to the same schools and had the same jobs as everybody else, and nobody spoke about our ancestry.

I used to go to see my grandmother, in my breaks from the University. It was pointless for me to visit her just for an afternoon or two. I would have to hang out for at least a week before our energies would mingle, she would open up, and really start talking to me. So I would find jobs to do, like painting her house or replacing her screens.

On one of those visits the subject came up. "You know we're Indian, don't you?" she confided.

"You?" I asked, astonished. "You always bad mouthed the Indians more than anybody!"

My grandmother chuckled slyly. "Pure self defense! When I was a girl, they were still killing anybody who had a drop of Indian blood."

I was surprised to discover, when I asked, that all four of my grandparents were half Native American.

Indigenous Americans have always survived by becoming invisible. In nature, that involved quieting the thoughts, stilling the mind until there was no separation from the environment, until one, in a sense, disappeared.

The old power spots, the favorite places in nature, are the sites of cities now. Almost every one is covered in concrete, except for the tiny refuges, the spots that could support only a few people. Faced with this new and alien man-made environment, some Native American families adapted by blending in without being noticed. My cultural heritage is in becoming socially invisible.

Two

September found me back at the University of Texas, sun-browned and fifteen pounds lighter from my two months in the desert. I had considered staying at the waterfall indefinitely, and knew that there was enough food to allow that possibility. But my curiosity drew me back to the world of people. I really wanted to understand my own species.

Something of the desert surrounded me, creating a gap, a bit of distance between myself and others. Yet the joy in their eyes over the smallest things, the conversations, the flirtations, all of it seemed so fresh and immensely beautiful to me.

With this perspective, the relevance of what I was studying was easily questioned. Having been a science whiz as a kid, the space program had magnetized me for years. That was the frontier for my entire generation. There was a heady feeling of excitement surrounding the exploration of space that had fueled my study of math and science.

Now, contrasted with my own inner exploration, I began to feel the limitations of knowledge. The further I went in math, the more specific and constricted it became. It was easy to see the practicality of science, living in a world suffused with technology. But somehow the examination of the physical universe had lost touch with the mystery at its core. That mystery was alive and breathing in people, so I decided to study them instead. I was well on my way to my degree in physics when my focus shifted to psychology.

I studied Freud, Jung, Rogers, Maslow. I watched my teachers closely, and befriended many of them. Although I had great respect for their knowledge, I couldn't shake the feeling that they were not transformed, in any fundamental way, by all they knew.

The elaborate imagery of the Jungians ignited the artists and dancers, and helped to fuel a grand explosion of creativity. Austin, Texas in the early '70s was alive with every sort of expression. I loved the free-spirited, vibrant energy of the place.

道

Sheri was six feet, nearly as tall as I was, with a mane of dark hair to her waist. On stage, you couldn't take your eyes off her. She was a naturally gifted actress, with the self contained presence of a lion. I was fascinated.

The first time I went to visit her, we sat together on the porch swing, watching the evening light wane. She seemed something of a contradiction to me. Sheri was almost old fashioned, in some respects. But her intelligence and stunning physical presence gave her a visceral quality that didn't quite fit within the confines of her Southern Baptist upbringing.

She asked penetrating questions, and was unsatisfied with easy answers. She really wanted to know who I was, what was important to me.

As her questions took me to a deeper level, I began to identify with my experience at Lake Travis. I swam as frequently as possible at that magical lake. I loved going there at daybreak, alone, touching the gold and rose clouds mirrored over the surface of the cool water. I felt the changing mood of the lake, sometimes opaque, at other times transparent, reflecting the distant mountains on the far shore, almost like sensing the mood of a lover. It was something of a love affair, my relationship with that lake.

Well, Lake Travis was what I started talking about, when Sheri asked me what I really cared for. Somehow, that created a connection, an understanding between us. We decided to go there together, the next morning.

That lake touched a silence within Sheri, an elemental part of her being that made her want to return again and again. Still, she was not quite comfortable with the raw power of the place. I could see her struggle with it, struggling with her own awakening power.

I was disappointed to see that Sheri had a stranger at her house, a robust friend named Joe who obviously knew her well. I had come unannounced, but I accepted a chair, sat quietly, and waited for him to leave.

My entrance barely caused a pause in the conversation. The fellow talked exuberantly about all kinds of things, and I wondered how long it would take him to run out of steam. He started talking about Tai Chi, which I knew nothing about, and finally asked me to stand up and help demonstrate a two person form called push-hands.

I figured that was a step in the right direction. If he was on his feet, he might leave. With that thought in mind, I stood up. Joe placed the back of his wrist against the back of my wrist, and demonstrated the simple circular Tai Chi motion.

Suddenly, I felt like I was back in the desert again. Silence. That feeling of inner peace, so strongly associated with being alone in nature, was what I felt for a brief moment. I was stunned to feel it, even a glimpse of it, here in the midst of the city, with another person, especially this talkative character. Joe caught my eye. He paused briefly in his monologue, recognizing that something had just passed between us.

Before long, Joe was out the door, still talking. He went back to California and I didn't see him again for a whole year.

When Joe returned to Austin, he began to teach Tai Chi. We both remembered that moment we first connected, and I wanted to take his class.

I found Tai Chi frustrating at first. I didn't take to it naturally, the way I did with most sports or physical activities. In the first class, Joe talked about moving energy in the body, and I left feeling like I just didn't get it. The slow, detailed movements were somehow beyond my grasp, although they weren't really difficult to perform. Clearly, this was a different kind of learning than mere choreography.

After that first class, feeling kind of clumsy and uncoordinated, I stood at the street corner, waiting for the traffic light to change. I looked down at my hands, wondering if I'd ever actually feel energy circulating through them the way Joe described. I wondered what part imagination played in this, and how much was a physical reality.

As I stood there looking at my hands, the thought arose, 'I wish I'd started this when I was six years old.' Even though I was only twenty, something about this was so valuable that I should have started years before. So I found myself both intrigued and frustrated, all at the same time.

Somehow I stuck with it, and over the next few weeks and months my practice began to take hold. It was a slippery thing to learn, though. Every time I thought I knew something, I would realize I didn't know it at all. Learning had always come easily to me, but this seemed to be engaging me on a whole new level. I loved the daybreaks, when I rode my bike to the park, climbed to my favorite hill, and practiced Tai Chi as the sun rose over the city. The beauty of those early mornings kept me going.

Joe and I were pretty evenly matched in physical strength and in overall tenacity as well. The first time we went out to eat, he didn't realize that I'd been swimming for four hours that day, and had ridden my bike twenty miles. He was stunned to find another human being who could out eat him, both in speed and quantity.

Joe's friend arrived, and remarked that it was the first time he'd ever seen Joe not talking. Joe laughed, "I don't have to talk around Tom. He knows how to be silent. Don't you realize my talking is just a defense?" He grinned. "If I have to hear anyone talking, I'd rather it be me, because I'm certainly more interesting than most of what I hear!"

This happened to be true. His discourses were characterized by an expansive humor that counterbalanced their frequency and duration. Joe had grown up in Chicago, and possessed an innate understanding of politics, social interactions, and peoples' motivations. This was all new to me.

Our friendship was a mutual learning. He introduced me to the world of people; I showed him the world of nature. Tai Chi was the medium of our exchange.

Although we began to spend more and more time in our practice of Tai Chi, we still lived the same lifestyle as any young men in the '70s in a college town. Our relationships were still reflective of our age group.

My relationship with Sheri had grown closer. She was drawn to the part of my nature that she couldn't understand, the wild spirit that made me seek isolation in the desert. That was what magnetized her, yet it bedeviled our communication, as well. She could never fathom what it was that guided my decisions, that shaped my priorities. And I was too unripe to explain myself to her.

This rift surfaced, over seemingly trivial matters, when we endeavored to live together. Although there are many fine memories of that venture, the one that is strongest happened late one summer night, when I returned home with Joe well after midnight. I had called to let Sheri know that the Linda Ronstadt concert we had gone to see had started hours later than scheduled. She was annoyed. She was involved with a theater production, and had been unable to go with us, and wanted me to go with her instead. Women's reactions often mystified me, and this was no exception.

As we pulled in the driveway, Joe was saying that he'd come in and say hello to Sheri. We both looked up to see the whole house ablaze with lights. The upstairs windows were wide open, and objects were sailing through the air. Colors and shapes kept flying out the window. As they fell past the windowsill, they turned into these dark amorphous silhouettes, which I suddenly noticed were scattered all across my lawn. With a sinking feeling, I realized that all my possessions were being unceremoniously jettisoned from that upstairs window.

A pregnant pause elapsed as we both stared at my belongings lying on the grass. With deliberate understatement, Joe announced, "Well, I won't be coming in tonight."

"Maybe I should leave with you?" I asked hope-fully, wishing for a way to avoid the inevitable.

"Na, go on in now. Get it over with," Joe was not unkind, but I couldn't help feeling that he was some-how amused by my predicament.

This rather chaotic period in my personal life left space for the next phase to unfold. Joe and two other friends had just opened a trendy little gourmet cheese shop called 'Quel Fromage,' and we decided to go in on a little eatery right behind. This suggested the name of the place, which was 'Cafe Derriere.'

This cafe was my little project, and I wanted to make the decor as inventive and colorful as the cheese store. So I stripped some weathered boards off of old barns, and nailed them to the walls in irregular pat-terns. I painted the floor with the same patterns, but in deep, muted shades, with a high gloss finish. It gave the impression of a deep reflecting pool, mirroring the arrangement of wood on the walls.

At the start of this project, I spent an entire day scrubbing piles of weathered lumber from a barn I'd torn down. I worked under a big tree, right outside the cheese shop, taking a hose and metal scrub brush to this heap of old wood.

Towards late afternoon I heard a tap on the window, and looked up to see a sight I'll never forget. What I took at first to be a grotesquely misshapen face was pressed against the side window of the cheese store. I couldn't quite make out what I was seeing, then I glanced toward the next window, which also displayed a large slab of folded flesh plastered against the windowpane. "What the heck is that?" I muttered. The third window likewise contained a blob of skin flattened against the glass. By this time, I recognized my three friends, Joe and our two business partners. In this unaccustomed view, their three bums were mooning me in the fancy art deco windows, right under the newly painted sign for 'Cafe Derriere.'

Finally, we got the place finished, and that old building was transformed. I'd certainly never seen any structure that looked the way that one did. The moldings around the French doors were painted in four different shades of peach and rose, and the exterior was the most whimsical combination of pastels. I don't know where Joe got the idea for those colors. It must have been from his travels in Europe or else some dream he had, but the result was definitely eye-catching.

The place just boomed as soon as we opened the doors. The *Texas Monthly*, which is a local version of *The New Yorker*, wrote us up in their 'Tout' section several times, but it was mostly just word of mouth. We started out with seating for fifteen, but immediately expanded to forty-five, opening up a patio out back. It was standing room only most times in the cheese shop, and we served over two hundred lunches out of our tiny little kitchen on a good day.

We had a good friend, a really talented dance teacher named Punkie. He took such a shine to the place, he asked us if he could wait tables. Now Punkie had acted on Broadway for years, had a good job teaching dance at the University, and certainly didn't need to be waiting tables. But he just kind of liked the idea somehow. I got a kick out of watching Punkie at work. He pranced through that crowded restaurant like it was an elaborate stage set, pirouetting his entrance to every table, dressed like some exotic dervish. Punkie had such a riveting stage presence, and his gestures and movements were so inventive, that everybody's eyes just naturally followed him as he traversed the room.

When Punkie took over as head waiter, he brought with him an entire cast of characters. He'd have friends come visit him from New York, dancers and actors, some of them quite famous, and they'd all end up at our place. So we fixed up a marquee announcing the 'Waiter of the Day' with the name of whomever happened to be visiting. Some of them would actually get in there and help Punkie wait tables, but most of them just hung out at the bar and entertained the customers.

Our place was in an old neighborhood just walking distance from the capital building in Austin, and all the lawyers, secretaries and business people used to flock there for lunch. Once, our banker was there with a table full of his cocky and rather demanding friends. They came in the dead center of our lunch rush, and we were slinging food out of that little kitchen as fast as humanly possible. Punkie heard these stuffed shirts grumbling every time he whirled past their table. Finally, he snapped. Coming to an abrupt stop, he drew up to his full height, composing himself as elegantly as if he were entering a Broadway stage. In his most commanding delivery, he pronounced, "If you want fast service, there's a greasy spoon downtown where you can poison yourself. If you want to eat here, shut up and wait your turn!" With that, he turned curtly on his heel, leaving them stunned.

Joe and I heard that, turned to each other, and just broke loose. We laughed until tears ran down our faces. The whole thing just seemed hysterical to us.

Right across from the shop was a big old colonial style house, where Joe and I lived. It had huge verandas, both upstairs and down, that ran the entire length of the house, with columns about two and a half feet wide. The upstairs veranda, which was as big as some entire houses, was screened in, and one corner was fitted with closing glass windows. I slept in that room for years, and never once shut the windows. I just put an extra blanket on the bed when it got cold.

Our house was perched on one hill, and the capital building sat on another. The whole area was full of small businesses, and our friends and customers would walk by our house and shop every morning on their way to work.

They'd see Joe and me out in the big backyard, doing our Tai Chi practices, our sword forms, throwing knives, and engaged in our archery tournaments. We set up targets on the side of the barn, and marked out an obstacle course around the old trees in our yard. We warmed up by doing standing shots, then we'd mount five arrows on our backs, and time each other as we ran the course. We'd jump on our bellies and shoot under a shrub in one spot, and then hop up on a low branch and aim from there, then shoot arrows through the crack between two trunks in another place. We'd always get to yelling and hollering at each other.

I'm not quite sure what people thought was going on there, but the net effect was that we never had to lock the doors. In fact, no one would even walk up onto our porch without announcing themselves from the road first. They all figured the place was armed in every conceivable way. Consequently, I never even had a key to that house, in all the years I lived there.

People must have thought all kinds of things about that crazy household. Lots of people assumed we were gay because Joe and I spent so much time together. We got quite a kick out of that, and it actually worked in our favor, because women were more comfortable around us.

Three

As my Tai Chi training continued, it began to shape my life in subtle ways. I realized that awareness training was the simple act of remaining undistracted with all the details of each moment. Simply observing. As this continued, I felt myself becoming more sensitive, more alert to subtle changes. With this increased sensitivity and deeper listening comes more and more detailed information.

This is where intuition became important. Intuition is the capacity to instantly summarize information in a succinct form without analysis. This frees the mind from its normal clutter of thoughts, allowing space for silence and listening. As silence deepens, intuition begins to change to clarity.

The key to all of this is relaxation and letting go of the outcome. This whole process begins when we realize our potential is lying dormant and the desire arises to activate it.

I devoted several hours at sunrise, at least six days a week, and I noticed that if I'd had any alcohol or any drug, even the smallest amount, my practice regressed quite strongly. My awareness just wasn't as clear. My sensitivity was diminished. Since my meditation was much more important to me than my social life, it wasn't even a choice, really. It certainly wasn't an ethical or moral question. It simply became apparent that any kind of mind altering substance was incompatible with a spiritual practice.

This was the early '70s, and a college town, where people were experimenting with various kinds of drugs, particularly hallucinogens. There was a common idea, propagated by Aldous Huxley and Timothy Leary, that drugs were the fast track to achieving spiritual experiences. Many of the people I knew had these magical mystery tours, these fantastic journeys to relate. They felt themselves expanding through space and time, becoming one with the stars, travelling up one side of reality and down the other.

But what I noticed was how scattered they became after those experiences. Their sensitivity was more constricted than before the drug trip. The field of awareness itself was actually sacrificed in order to experience these fantasies. What fascinated me was how the person never seemed to notice their own shrunken capacities, in the enthusiasm for their dreams. I felt that many of these people were motivated by a genuine thirst for spirituality in their lives, for a glimpse of a larger reality, but drugs offered a false coin, a mirage. These drug experiences are a mind trip, a projection having nothing to do with reality, and seemed to me to be an enormous diversion.

A lot of dancers, musicians, and artists, the most creative people I knew, had trouble understanding Tai Chi. They could see no point in practicing a repetitive series of movements, but wanted instead to do something new and different, preferably something that had never been done before. The focus of dance generally is to perform, to express something outwardly, while Tai Chi is an inward turning.

Of all the hundreds of thousands of times I've done the Tai Chi form, it's never felt the same way twice. The value of that training for me was in developing the sensitivity to perceive those subtle nuances. Rather than creating something in the external world, like a work of art or dance, Tai Chi created something within me, the capacity to witness my own consciousness, and the means to nurture that growth. To me, that's the epitome of creativity.

While I started to learn more about my own energy through Tai Chi, it was push-hands that taught about the subtleties of relating to other people. This two person form is where the practice most closely mirrors the ordinary world of daily interactions.

When you first see it, push-hands is deceptively simple. Two people stand facing each other, with the backs of their wrists touching. They move through this little circular pattern together, not moving the feet. In its basic form, it's a simple rounded motion, with only the backs of the hands touching, about as gently as one might touch the wing of a butterfly.

When I first tried it, I was completely baffled. We'd be going around in a circle and then suddenly I'd have to take a step or two to keep from falling over. "It's always your own energy that throws you off balance," Joe commented.

That simple observation seemed to hold true. Just like in ordinary life, when you're too pushy, you get thrown off balance. But if you collapse your space, you're going to find yourself off center as well. So the idea is to keep engaging, keep interacting, without compromising the integrity of your own physical space, and without over extending either. The practice teaches you not to anticipate, not to get ahead of yourself, but to respond exactly to what's occurring in the moment. It's a brilliant way to learn sensitivity in human interactions.

But it took me a long time to figure all that out. I had no idea what we were supposed to be trying to do, and at first I assumed it was somehow about winning and losing. But that very notion made me predictable, produced automatic, mechanical reactions in me. I'd be thrown off balance immediately.

Eventually I learned to let go, to relax, to virtually disappear, while continuing to engage at the same time. Push-hands helped erase the force of habit that made me respond to the world in a set pattern. Before push-hands, when a new situation confronted me, I had a tendency to resist while attempting to understand it. This attempt to keep something at a distance while slowly absorbing it, created a backlog.

Push-hands taught me to let go, and allow the energy to pass through me. This instantly created the proper response and a complete understanding of what was occurring. It was enormously useful, but that took many, many years to develop.

I was no good at letting go when I started. Because I was accustomed to physical strength and a forceful personality, this response was completely foreign to me.

One day, Joe and I were working with a class of beginning students in the park. It was late afternoon, the heat of the day had softened, and we were all gathered in the shade of some large maple trees.

Joe and I were standing facing each other in front of the class, ready to engage in push-hands. "In a moment when we start, push harder than usual," he told me, wanting to make the point visibly to the new students. I had already learned to quit pushing hard against him, since every time I did, I lost my balance with the the returning energy. But he wanted to make the demonstration dramatic and obvious for the students. His body was facing me, but his head was turned to the side, talking. As he was explaining the subtleties of push-hands, I was chuckling to myself, thinking, "This might be my chance! I've never been able to throw this guy off, even a little. I wonder what would happen..."

Joe kept talking, facing the students, our hands in contact about heart level as we began to cycle. As my weight came up off my back foot, my hands lifted toward his throat. I lunged into him with all my weight and all my strength. Although he weighed slightly more, I was probably physically stronger. I totally thought I had him.

Joe's conversation never broke stride. As my hands came forward, his palms came under my elbows. He simply released and moved like a door revolving. He could have slung me 20 feet, I came at him so hard. Holding my elbows with open palms, he started turning round and round, whirling me like a little kid. My feet were sailing through the air, at least three full revolutions. In his kindness, Joe was dissipating my energy, and I touched the ground softly as a leaf fallen from a tree.

I burst out laughing, lying on the ground, feeling about five years old. Joe was still talking, making his point without interruption.

He looked down at me, "Do you know what just happened?"

"I don't know what happened, but I want to do it again!"

I got better, I hope, at push-hands. We practiced early mornings in the park near a natural spring that fed a huge swimming pool. When Joe figured he'd had enough and was ready to go on about his day, he would put me with my back to the pool. "Ready to go for a swim?" he'd grin.

I knew that the next time I didn't release the energy, I'd find myself flying into the water. So that was the ultimate challenge, which usually lasted about three seconds. Sometimes I could go 15 or 20 seconds, and I'd feel pretty good about that. That was Joe's way of making me pay more attention.

He'd dive in right after me, and we'd take our morning swim.

After practicing with Joe for two or three years, he began having me teach. Typically, my introduction to teaching Tai Chi caught me by surprise. Joe simply didn't arrive. We had four consecutive classes scheduled in the park, and the first group was ready to go. Since I had been the assistant, demonstrating up front while he taught, the students wanted me to go ahead and start the class. We all figured he'd be along any second. That never happened, and I ended up leading all four classes. It was more demanding than I realized.

Joe was sitting on the front steps waiting for me when I got home. "Be prepared to teach every day from now on. Sometimes I may tell you, sometimes not. See, I told you it was hard work! Be prepared. How did it go?"

It was very easy to doubt the whole concept of internal energy, even after I'd been experiencing the health benefits and relaxation of Tai Chi for a few years. It seemed hard to tell if I was feeling something real, or if my imagination created what I was sensing. That's how subtle it is. So I expect other people to come at this whole notion with a good deal of distrust, as well.

Joe and I were teaching a class full of doubters, students who were even more skeptical than average.

Joe suggested we try a little experiment. He and I stood facing each other, with the others gathered all around. He placed his palms down, with my palms up directly beneath them, so our hands were facing each other. He told one of the students to stand behind him and to tap either his left or right shoulder blade, and that's the side he would direct his energy toward. While my eyes were closed, I was supposed to be able to sense which of his hands was full of energy.

"Yeah, right," I thought. "I'm going to blow this one completely." The students were looking for hidden signals, gestures with the eyes, a nod of the head.

I just closed my eyes and relaxed. It was almost as if each of my closed eyes was looking into a darkened room, and then the flicker of a candle approached the left side. The light got stronger, and I tapped with my left hand.

As I kept my eyes closed, the light dimmed to just a flicker. A long time passed, several minutes. Finally the light reentered, again on the left side. I tapped.

This time the light disappeared, and then jumped back immediately to the left side. I tapped with my hand, but then dropped my hands, apologizing.

"Sorry, guys, I know I'm just making a mess out of this."

They were all stunned. They had been trying to trick me by having that long pause in between, to see if I'd tap while nothing was happening. I'd gotten it exactly right.

Joe had me continue this exercise, about twenty more times. Then we reversed hands, with someone tapping my shoulder blades in a different sequence, and I directed my energy, which Joe read easily. Neither one of us made a single mistake.

After taking part in that demonstration, I couldn't deny this stuff to myself any longer. Internal energy was real, something you actually can learn to experience and to direct.

A few months later, Joe and I were teaching two classes in a large auditorium. He was working with the intermediate students, while I was leading the beginners. It was my first experience with starting a class of newcomers from scratch.

I had a bum knee that I'd injured playing football, then reinjured mountain climbing, and then strained again riding rodeos. It had bothered me quite a bit for several years.

In teaching, I was exaggerating the movements so the internal flow of energy would be visible to the students. I shifted all my weight to my left foot, and suddenly found myself literally on the ground writhing in pain, holding onto my left leg. It felt just like I'd completely blown out my bad knee.

Joe and all his students gathered around, with my own class, wondering what on earth had happened. Slowly I began to realize that this had a different quality than the other times I'd injured my knee. Something told me that, in spite of the pain, this was going to work out all right.

I took a moment and made sure I could actually bend my leg and stand up again. Then I immediately began circulating the energy through the hip, through the knee, and down to the ball of the foot, then back up and down the other side.

What had happened was that I was releasing the injury, and in doing so, I was reexperiencing it. This was actually a healing crisis, rather than another injury. I have seen Tai Chi heal wounds both physical and emotional, and it often has this pattern. Although it feels as if the injury has reoccurred, in fact the trauma has resurfaced, and is ready to be released.

I taught the rest of that class, without further pain. Joe suggested a Tai Chi meditation for me to try while lying flat on my back, before going to sleep.

I started by circulating the energy of the breath through the body. First I emptied all the excess energy back to the center, or the dantien, which is located two inches below the navel. That point, also known as the hara, is like grand central station for the energy system. This Tai Chi meditation can take around twenty minutes to complete.

Then I would take that energy from the center, through the hip, knee, ankle, out the bottom of the foot, back into the other foot, ankle, knee, hip, returning to the hara. That orbit created a circle of energy that kept travelling through the injured knee, and back to the center.

I did that for a month with little apparent result. One night, I wasn't quite as sleepy. I managed to get the circulation going very strongly, and kept it going quite a long time before falling asleep. I woke up the next morning with a start, bolting out of bed, and landed in the middle of the floor. It felt like something alive was crawling on my legs, maybe a snake or an insect. Looking down, I realized the sensation was continuing. The orbit of energy had been so strongly established that it had kept circulating all night long.

My knee has been virtually pain free since that night, and now it's as strong as any other joint in my body.

Having these very internal experiences produce such real results began to make me more curious about Joe. How had he become interested in Tai Chi? I waited for the right moment and asked him.

He told me it happened when he was nine years old. He walked into the living room where his family was watching television and froze in place when he saw a group of people doing a series of movements together. As the image on the screen changed, he asked his family what the movements were called. No one else had paid much attention, but they thought it was a Korean folk dance.

For the next ten years, Joe learned all he could about Asian folk dances. None was even vaguely like what that boy had seen on TV that evening in Chicago. He was on the wrong track, but was sure that it was only a matter of time.

At age 20, he enrolled at California Institute of the Arts and learned that all the students were required to study something called Tai Chi. He was interested in becoming an actor and director. What did Tai Chi have to do with that? Entering the first class brought forth the same reaction that nine year old boy had felt. As he stood there in the grip of this second experience looking back in time to his younger self, he realized that even further back in time were other moments like these two.

As all the questions that this vision evoked began to rush into his mind, he was startled back to reality. The class was beginning. He didn't yet know the answers to all those questions. He did know he was in the right place...again.

All his teachers were pleasantly surprised at how quickly he mastered the movements. Even more surprising was the depth of understanding he displayed in the knowledge that lives behind the movements.

When I first watched Joe perform these slow, dance like movements of Tai Chi, I thought that perhaps it was a warm up, a prelude to a martial art. What affect could this possibly have in a real life situation? It just didn't seem plausible. Over the years I never understood it logically, but I did have the opportunity to see it function in surprising ways.

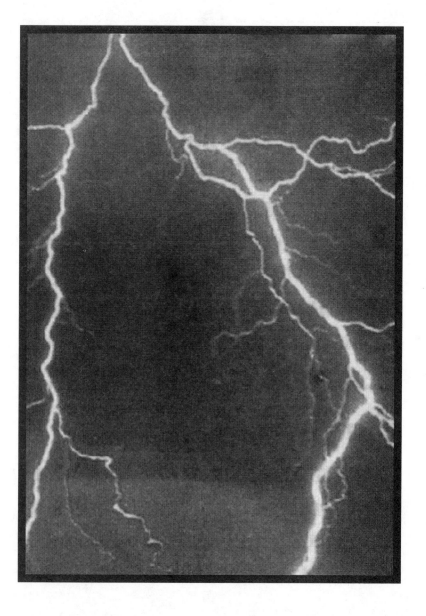

Four

I stayed in New York City for several months, at one time, and studied with a Tai Chi master in his mid-70's. He asked four of us from his class to help him move out of his apartment up two flights of stairs to another place, which he was going to use while his flat was being refurbished. It took us about an hour and a half to move his things. But we all kept avoiding the refrigerator, because it was so unwieldy to muscle all the way up those stairs. Two of us could have lifted it, but we were all hoping it would be someone else.

"You guys still have a lot to learn!" Suddenly he was the teacher again.

This tiny old man walked up, extended his arms and lightly touched the sides of the refrigerator. He didn't hug it, but left a gap of at least six inches between it and his body. He settled in the same sinking movement that occurs throughout the Tai Chi form. When he rose up, the refrigerator lifted off the ground, and he proceeded to carry the thing up two flights of steps. It never so much as leaned against his chest, and his arm muscles were completely relaxed the entire time. It was pure energy!

I saw what happened, but hesitated for years to even tell the story. I could scarcely believe it myself, and I had seen it with my own eyes. We've all heard stories of a mother lifting a car off her child, but this had no such emotional charge or adrenalin rush.

I have witnessed things occurring with Tai Chi that totally defy my rational understanding. That's why I often recommend that anyone who's interested should begin by committing six months to attending classes, rather than trying to read about it and understand it intellectually.

Another situation occurred after we opened the cafe and cheese shop. Joe and I used to go to the auctions, where we picked up restaurant equipment for the business and our house.

Joe bought an enormous industrial wooden chopping block, which was well used, and greasy. We were moving it into the kitchen of our house with a dolly. Three of us had managed to get this 350 lb. block up the steps and into the house. An old fashioned floor jamb leading into the kitchen was what finally broke the dolly, and the block fell flat on the kitchen floor.

The three of us decided we'd wait until there was a fourth person to help, so the block remained in the middle of our kitchen floor until the next day.

Joe and I had our early Tai Chi practice and swim, then headed back to the house. Joe motioned toward the block, "It's about time you learn something. We'll see if you can do this or not."

I didn't know what he was talking about.

"We're going to lift this chopping block, just the two of us. We're going to do it with no muscles and no effort."

To me, that seemed impossible, but I didn't mind trying, because the worst that would happen was that our fingers would slip off. What made it so awkward to lift was that the block was flush to the floor, with no space for a hand hold, nowhere to get any grip at all.

"I want you to look right at me." Joe said. "Don't take your eyes off my eyes. Breathe exactly together, so energy is generated not only within our own bodies, but between us. We're going to do three deep breaths, and then we're going to bend from the knees, and touch the sides of the chopping block with our fingers. Don't use any effort. When you start the exhale, we'll stand up together, and set the chopping block on its stand."

I now teach this breathing technique as Chi Kung, but Joe at that time referred to them as Zen breathing exercises. Joe's presence was so strong, and we had years of practicing and training together. I could feel myself slip into an altered state energetically. It felt like a web of energy between my hands and between the two of us, extending beneath that 350 lb. block, which lifted like a feather. The muscles in my arms were limp, not even engaged.

That was the same logic defying occurrence I'd witnessed in New York, and here I was participating in it.

Shortly afterwards, I went out to get some tools out of my truck. Our front porch was about twelve steps up, quite high off the ground. Since I was young and didn't know better, I used to leap over the railing, landing on the lawn, instead of using the stairs.

The energy exchange that allowed us to lift the chopping block affected me more than I realized. I approached the railing with my normal momentum, planted my left hand, and swung over. I was astonished to see three feet of air between my hand and the railing. I had jumped three feet higher than I normally would have, well beyond my normal capacity to jump. This maneuver left me flying through the air, losing my balance, and heading for the rosebushes. I managed to throw myself into a roll, compensating for the momentum, and avoiding the thorns. Joe happened to walk out on the porch behind me, and commented calmly, "Well, you make a lot of mistakes, but you're quick to recover."

At the time, this incident was one of a group of curious anomalies that seemed to happen with no effort on my part. I didn't quite know what to make of these extraordinary events, but they seemed more interesting and somehow significant than the normal world. It wasn't until much later, after nearly losing my life, that I realized how unimportant these things really were.

I went through a period of several months when I had the sensation of seeing the future. I would hear a knock on the door, and turn to go answer it. In the split second it took to turn my head, I knew who was at the door, what they were wearing, what they would say, and the events that would unfold for the rest of the afternoon.

People sometimes would ask about the weather, figuring that somehow I knew about these things. Once it had been raining for five days in Texas, which usually gets only brief thunderstorms and passing showers. A friend asked me, "You're in touch with the elements. When's it going to stop raining?"

"In thirteen days, at 2:00 in the afternoon." I had never even considered this question before, and had absolutely no interest in it, but the answer just popped out of my mouth.

"You sure you want to say that? Thirteen days? It seems impossible!" My friend looked a bit disconcerted, almost like I'd let him down by giving such a wildly improbable answer. But you know, that's exactly the day and the hour the rains stopped.

One morning I called a friend, and asked her if she wanted to go to the lake with me. I had a lot to do, and she had even more to do, but I really wanted to go for a swim anyway. "Well, it's windy outside. It's not that much fun when it's so windy at the lake." She was ready to dismiss the idea.

"You take care of the things you have to do, and I'll take care of the weather," I said, flippantly. She laughed, and agreed to go.

The cool waters of the lake were more beautiful than ever that day. We swam lazily together, then lay across the warm rocks to bask in the sun. The air was crisp, with fleecy white clouds against a radiant blue sky.

"Didn't I tell you I'd take care of the weather?" I chided her, grinning. Without even looking over at me, she continued to gaze up into the clear air. She calmly lifted her hand toward the sky, and held it perfectly still. I followed her gesture with my eyes, and saw a delicate yellow butterfly about thirty feet above us. We both watched silently as those tiny patterned wings fluttered down and landed on her outstretched finger. Without a word, she reached over and set the butterfly on my navel, as if to say, "We all do these things." It was instantly humbling.

I understood her message, and while I felt a bit foolish at the time, it was a gentle reminder not to take these things too seriously.

Years ago, when I used to dream, I dreamed I was in a large, crowded elevator. At every stop, people would get off. There were floors of practical experiences, floors of adventure, emotional, playful floors. The crowd thinned out at every stop. Finally, we came to the floor of psychic phenomenon. The door opened, and I could see that area was full of engaging toys, astral projection, telepathy, and the like. But very clearly that was not my floor. I stayed in the elevator alone, and that door closed.

I avoided getting entangled in this net of psychic abilities by not getting too concerned with them. It didn't matter if any of these phenomena ever happened again. It can be a major distraction, and a more difficult one to deal with than the normal problems of life.

道

Joe was invited to teach at a martial arts dojo, and he asked me to come along as an assistant. The head teacher was a marine who had served two terms in

Vietnam, he had used his training in hand-to-hand combat, and he taught a hard style fighting form. Some of his buddies from Vietnam joined him to teach in his school, so they had a very strong bond between them. These were good guys, very likable men, and several of them eventually became our friends.

There were 18 black belt teachers, and they were excellent at winning competitions. But the head of the school felt that they were getting off balance, and he wanted them to learn Tai Chi to soften their approach. He required all of the teachers to take Joe's Tai Chi class. About half of them would have been interested anyway, and the other half came only because they had to.

Over the first several weeks with Joe teaching, and me tagging along, we could feel an underlying resentment building. These were good fighters, men who already knew quite a lot about their practice. But they would be just beside themselves when we started push-hands. It seemed like child's play, it was so soft. They knew how to throw a punch or a kick, they knew how to win! Tai Chi just seemed irrelevant.

One morning, we came in and started our warm ups. "Let's do push-hands," Joe suggested, knowing that was exactly what they didn't want to do. They'd had enough of all that soft stuff.

Joe turned to the class, "None of you believe this, do you?" They didn't say anything, but it was clear that was true. One man slightly nodded his head. They had so much training about respecting whoever was teaching, that Joe had to prod them, "Come on, talk to me!" Finally one spoke up, saying that they didn't see anything but a child's game, nothing that would benefit them to learn.

Joe selected the best of them, not the head of the school, but the best of the 18 teachers, the one who won most of the individual competitions, to step forward.

Joe stood in a cycling position, his arms round as if he was holding a big invisible beach ball, his hands six or eight inches apart.

"I'm just going to stand here. I'm not going to hurt you, or try to retaliate. I'm not going to do anything. But I want you to punch and kick me. Try to knock me down. Try to win."

This guy didn't quite know what to do. He was standing there in front of all of his friends, on the spot. He started off with a few punches, not very seriously. Joe easy warded them off, and released the energy. He relaxed, rolled a little, but didn't even move his feet.

The guy got more serious, so he started shoving and punching a little, throwing a few kicks. Nothing seemed to be working. Joe wasn't doing anything but releasing, letting the punches roll off of him. A fist would touch him, but seemed to slide off his body, with no impact. Everything was being neutralized.

The fighter started doing different combinations of punches and kicks, as he got more intent. There's a fancy kick where the left foot acts as a range-finder, making contact with the opponent. Then the right foot follows through and actually delivers the blow.

When I saw him start with that kick, I knew he was in trouble. Joe allowed the left foot to touch his chest, which let the guy think he had him. When the right foot left the ground, Joe simply melted away. That guy's sheer momentum, kicking air, landed him flat on his back. You could hear how hard he hit the ground.

Here was the best of the black belts lying flat, out of breath, and Joe was standing above him in the same stance he'd started. He never so much as shifted his feet. He simply absorbed and released the energy.

The fighter seemed more bewildered than upset. Joe looked down at him, and across at the other 17, saying softly, "If you want to fight, fight with yourselves. If you want to learn something, I'll be glad to teach you."

Maybe it was simply testosterone expressing itself in the form of competitiveness, but it's not uncommon for Tai Chi to be viewed in terms of power. As a martial art, it is quite effective. Strictly as a fighting style, a practitioner does not reach his peak until the age of fifty or sixty. Sometimes students get sidetracked by powers of a more extraordinary type, by the capacity to do things that seem miraculous or supernatural.

But all of this is a diversion, the way I see it. Power, in any of its forms, is not the point. By even paying attention to that, you lose sight of the real gem, which is the awareness training.

Tai Chi, is a moving meditation which, at its highest levels, has the capacity to cleanse the senses, to break the routines of habit that dull the perceptions, and to awaken a vibrant consciousness that makes all of life a celebration.

My favorite story of Tai Chi in action is one a student told years later. I was teaching a class, all people who were new to me. Someone asked about martial arts, and this woman told her story.

She lived in Washington D.C., and wanted to learn a self defense technique. She didn't know one style from another, but someone recommended a Tai Chi class, so she went. She felt disappointed, because she didn't feel like she was learning a martial art. She hadn't learned any moves for defending against an attacker. But she rather enjoyed it, and was feeling less tension, less like she had to fight her way through life. She'd been studying about six months, and was feeling the benefits of relaxation more than anything else.

She pulled up into her driveway one night, and got out of the car, with two bags of groceries, one in each arm. Her purse was slung over one shoulder, and she had just locked her car door. She turned, not knowing there was a man who had appeared right behind her. He had been waiting for her, and she had no idea he was even there. The man yanked her purse, hoping to pull her down, to break the strap, to steal the purse. When he pulled, he automatically expected resistance. Instead, the opposite happened. She just relaxed and backed up with the pull. The man had pulled so hard, he fell over backwards, hitting his head on the concrete, knocking himself out briefly. She simply walked up the steps, unlocked the door, set down her groceries, and called the police. The man was apprehended not far from her house.

It wasn't until after the police left that she really made the connection, that she understood that she had defended herself without once thinking about self defense, without even knowing what the right moves might be. Her teacher concurred, "That was exactly Tai Chi!" It has no thought, no preconceptions, no set idea of what you should do under particular circumstance. You simply respond to what occurs. She had responded brilliantly, not losing her groceries, her purse, her keys, or her composure, without consciously even knowing what was occurring.

道

One of the things I most enjoyed about Tai Chi was that it kept me out in nature. I used to practice on my favorite hill, starting a couple of hours before dawn on full moon nights. The glorious sight of the full yellow moon slipping into the plateau to the west, as the sun rose over the city in the east, was just too beautiful to miss. There was a tremendous sense of balance during those moments.

A visual balance of the sun and moon the same size in the morning sky. One appearing, the other disappearing. A sensual balance as one side of the body filled with energy while the other side emptied. An earthly balance as a man danced this eternal dance surrounded by trees on this hill that was held gently in the curving embrace of the river below. A river that was bathed in those soft, penetrating pinks and blues that only show themselves briefly on special mornings. This ribbon of sky appearing on earth softly touching the surface of the water and for a moment spreading its winding arms in an embrace of bliss.

Five

*H*unting was an important part of my connection to nature, until a couple of experiences bonded me with the animal world in a more direct way. After that, hunting was simply impossible.

Hunting was my source of food. An allergy to tetracycline, which is fed to cattle, led to skin rashes when I went in the sun. So beef was out. I had never particularly liked pork, and I knew from experience how chickens were raised, which made me never want to eat them at all. So I had decided years before that any meat I consumed would be what I hunted myself. It was a practical decision, mostly.

One day I was bird hunting with my Dad and my brother Dave. I had arrived for this three day hunt with very little rest, so I was tired to start with. It was on the second day, when we were scattered apart, that I found myself by a very inviting creek. I decided to stretch out in the shade of an oak tree, where I fell asleep for about half an hour.

I was in that half-awake state between sleep and waking, when a dove flew right overhead. My immediate reflex was to raise my gun and shoot. The bird fluttered to the ground not far from me.

Doves have a purplish hue to their feathers, a lavender aura that surrounds them when they're alive. When they die, their feathers are a flat, dull grey. Well, I watched this bird fall to the ground, and about five seconds later, I saw his spirit fly away. I actually saw the purple shadow leave his lifeless body.

That got me to thinking that there's a whole lot more to all of this than meets the eye. I didn't quite know what to make of it though, and the momentum of my hunting was so strong, that it continued.

The next experience happened when I took Joe on his first hunt with my father and Dave. We were after mouflon rams, the big Sicilian rams, which ran loose on this Texas ranchland. My Dad had never seen me hunt with bow and arrow, and was kind of dubious about the whole idea. So I took my rifle, but packed the bows in the truck as well.

Joe and I had incorporated a sort of athletic, improvisational Zen archery into our daily Tai Chi routine. We had targets set up in our back yard, and practiced shooting while lying on our sides, while on our hands and knees, shooting on the run. We used to shoot arrows in the dark. We'd start out at sunset, and keep shooting until we could no longer see the target, just aiming from memory.

Neither of us really knew how well we'd do in actual hunting with bows and arrows. It requires so much more skill, and you have to get much closer to the quarry.

We sighted the rams from about a mile away, through binoculars. Both Joe and I picked the individual animals we wanted, knowing it would be harder to get a particular animal rather than any out of the group.

We picked a spot with some brush where Joe and I hid, but the others didn't get quite out of sight by the time the animals approached. They got spooked, and by the time the herd passed us, they were on a dead run.

Now most kills with a bow and arrow are shot from less than ten yards away. Joe was about 45 yards away from his animal, five times the distance of an average archery shot.

When the herd stampeded past us, Joe stood up, pulled back his bow, and in my head, I thought, "Joe, there's no way!" He let loose that arrow and it landed in exactly the ram he'd chosen, within an inch of that animal's heart.

The ram walked another 20 yards with the arrow still in his side, then turned back to the spot where he'd been hit. Joe shot a second arrow directly through his heart. These were two of the best shots I've ever seen with a bow and arrow. He did one right after the other on his very first hunt!

My Dad and Dave were so impressed, each of them talked about it for the next five years. There wasn't a time I saw them that they didn't mention those two shots. They were so outstanding. Those two shots had come directly out of Tai Chi practice.

So then it was my turn. I didn't get a clear shot in that round, and it took us another three hours to get close enough for me to get a good aim at the one ram I'd chosen.

So finally I got a shot, which landed pretty close to his heart. He lay down, and I walked up to him, another arrow ready. The others came up behind me, but I motioned them to go away.

I pulled the dying ram onto my lap, holding his head on my one leg, his shoulders on the other. He looked straight into my eyes, and I looked into his. We held each others gaze, unwavering, for perhaps two or three minutes, not a short time. He was still, very still.

Suddenly he began to struggle in pain. I took my knife out and, while we looked into each others' eyes, I killed him.

The moment the animal died had a certain timelessness. It could have been 10,000 years ago or 1000 years ago. The Native people of this country, my American ancestors, had felt themselves intimately linked with nature. Something of themselves was killed when they hunted.

I was born under the sign of the ram. I felt like I was watching a part of myself die, a part that needed to die. Something about the dignity with which that animal died made me unafraid myself. The part of me that ended was my fear of death.

And a part of that ram lives in me, a part that needed to live. His joy, the freedom of running over the hills under the open sky, of nuzzling with his friends, of feeling the rain and the sun on his skin. I can feel his joy alive in me to this day.

After hunting had ended for me, there came a time in my Tai Chi practice where I didn't want to be around people at all. I felt such an expansiveness into nature, and other humans were an enormous distraction during those moments. I knew a place in a park where I could go every morning at dawn, and not see anyone for several hours.

The remarkable thing was that the animals stopped seeing me as human. When my Tai Chi was really working, when the boundaries between myself and the trees and the sky had dissolved, the wild creatures would approach me without fear. A rabbit literally hopped between my feet once when I was doing my temple exercises. I returned home that day and wrote the following poem.

MORNING

Standing in Tanaguchi Garden overlooking the city. I gaze at the maple tree I have come to know over the last four years. Although it is too early to see, I know that she is wearing her fall colors. Leaves rustle in the crisp air. The sun will rise soon. Near the waterfall I wash my hands and face. Clearing my eyes and leaving the dust of activity behind, I approach my spot. Settling in place, Tai Chi begins. Crane cools its wings, needle at sea bottom, fan through the back, parting the wild horses mane...one unfolds out of the other. The sun rises, the breeze changes, and energy ebbs and flows through the body. Birds call from the maple tree. Their sounds mix with those of the water.

Everything pauses. People enter the park. Odd sounds against silence. Listening to the approach. Ten minutes. Tai Chi continues. The hush lifts to the top of the trees and waits.

Soon.

Rabbits and squirrels begin to move away from the approaching rumble. Inbreath and outbreath - energy from the fingers and toes to the center. Rabbits standing between the feet, sheltered beneath the moving body. Silence dances and the song is heard throughout time. The movements end. All creatures disappear into the trees. I leave with the farewell rustle of the maple in my ears. The stream chuckles. A swirling of small birds. Another day starts with the communion of friends.

Six

knew I was sick. My body felt weak, and my energy was low, but I was used to powering through these things on sheer stamina. A friend who had gone with me to Mexico two weeks before thought she might have hepatitis, and was becoming quite ill. I decided to stop by the health clinic that afternoon.

Without much ado, they administered a shot of gamma globulin. That proved to be a nearly fatal mistake. I had already been exposed to hepatitis, and that injection dramatically complicated my condition.

I worked by myself all the next afternoon in the warehouse, and I started blacking out. I would come to and keep right on working. That's how stubborn I was. Truly stubborn.

Finally I went home to bed, feeling myself getting sicker by the hour. Three of us were sharing the house, Joe, a friend of ours who was a medical doctor, and I. It was about 6:00 in the evening, and neither of my housemates were home. I called my girlfriend, hoping she could come by to see me. Expecting her, I dozed off for a quick nap.

When I woke up, my first feeling was disappointment that my girlfriend wasn't there. Then I realized that it was late, about 1:00 in the morning. I had slept for seven hours.

Some dramatic change felt imminent. During the day, whenever I would start to pass out, it was like hearing a car coming in the distance. Then suddenly it would arrive and I would black out.

But when I woke up that night I could hear a freight train heading straight for me. Something much bigger was about to happen, and I knew I was about to pass out.

The whole atmosphere was overpowering, pressing in on the surface of my skin. I had never in my life felt worse. I went to stand up to go to the bathroom, but I couldn't stand up, I was too weak and too disoriented. Somehow I managed to crawl to the bathroom. I was shaking, throwing up, sweating profusely, and was sick in every conceivable way.

Water had always been a healing thing for me. When I used to hike through the sweltering desert heat, immersing myself in the cool waterfall was better than anything I could think of. That's what I needed now. My body was on fire with fever, and I figured that if I could immerse myself in water, it would revive me.

We had one of those old fashioned tubs with antiquated plumbing, and you had to keep monitoring the water temperature to get it just right because it kept changing.

I was alternating between vomiting and diarrhea, feeling almost too weak to move. So I just let the tub fill up, without paying enough attention to the water temperature.

Suddenly I felt a very strong body rush, almost a convulsion. I was collapsing, totally incapable of almost anything. At one point, I even tried to get a drink of water and I didn't have the strength to turn the faucet on before I collapsed again.

It seemed as if I was down to my last move. I knew I only had one move left.

In my fevered logic, I thought that if I could get myself into the water, I would be rejuvenated. I collapsed into the tub, not realizing that the water was scalding hot. My body involuntarily leapt back out of that tub, reacting before I even had time to think.

As I hurled over the side of the tub, my spirit left my body. In midair, I just simply flew right outside the confines of my own skin.

That particular moment, to this day, is tremendously instructive for me. One moment, I had been struggling in agony inside my body, and a moment later I found myself leaving. At that critical moment,

I could either let go or lose consciousness, those were my two options. After five years of Tai Chi practice, my consciousness was identified with my life energy more than it was with my physical body.

When all the energy rushed out of the body, my awareness stayed with the energy, rather than the body. That continuity of awareness was the most important element. I was aware of being in the body, I was aware as I was leaving the body, and I was aware of the events that occurred out of the body. Because of my Tai Chi training, there was no break in awareness. It's hard to describe the intensity of that moment. Every event of my life, from the strongest interaction to the simplest occurrence, came flying toward me.

Not only were all the events coming back as memories, but all of those images also had an energy component, and all that energy was coming back together too. That moment of death had the amount of energy equivalent to all the experiences of my entire life. All that energy put me into motion. It was like a movie run backwards. If you filmed a beautiful crystal vase falling and shattering into millions of pieces, and then you ran that film in reverse, that's the sensation I had. All those luminous jewels rushed together to become a flawless crystal form. Within this form was a whole lifetime, all the emotions, the actions, the memories. There was a certain sweetness about seeing it all together in this way.

There wasn't time to savor the sweetness, because a rapid change was beginning. Energy was coalescing. Not only memories and emotions rushed together, but the dynamic power of an entire lifetime had arrived. It catapulted me into motion.

I took my attention off the crystal vase that was my life, and looked upward, to see the light I was fast approaching. As soon as I saw this light filled opening, it became immediately clear that I'd made this passage many times before.

My earliest memory as a baby involved seeing this light. Throughout my life, whenever I would lie down to sleep, I would close my eyes and see a dark river flowing. Within this moving blackness would appear a whirlpool of light. I would release myself into that opening.

There was a sensation of intense speed, which carried me through that portal. I shot right through that and beyond.

I had the distinct impression that there are places to stop in that light, realms to be outside the body, which we think of as heavens. They seemed comforting, reassuring, but I didn't stop there. On passing through those realms, I just went into pure emptiness, which felt absolutely perfect.

It is impossible to convey the profound trust I felt. A newborn infant at its mother's breast could not be held any more lovingly than I was held by the universe at that moment. I'm calling it emptiness, because there were no features, no distinctions between something else and my essence. Another way to say it would be that I, the sense of a separate self, disappeared. All that was left was awareness, silence.

All my life there had been a heartbeat of this deep silence that lay behind everything else, at the root of all the events and experiences. But here I was encountering emptiness in its absolute purity. It was the very source of life, undiluted, fully expanded.

And then there was a sense of drifting. I felt drawn toward something. When I considered what was pulling me, I realized it was my own curiosity. I wondered if I could go back. I wondered if it was possible.

For a moment I could have dropped this curiosity, and melted back into the stillness. But with no motivation beyond a simple curiosity, the journey back had begun.

I had the sense of movement, and then suddenly, for the first time, I had a visual sensation. I saw the earth, with the moon beside it, from a perspective far distant in space. This jolted me. It was disconcerting, to say the least, to be so very far away, with no idea at all of how to get back down.

Without any transition of time, I went from seeing the earth, to being back in that bathroom, seeing my body collapsed face down on the floor. From a perspective near the ceiling I looked down on my own inert form. My skin was still wet from the bathtub, my hair dripping into a puddle on the tiles. I had no more idea of how to get back into my body than I did how to get back to the earth, but I wanted to try.

In my Tai Chi practice, we were working on getting energy to the tips of the fingers. We'd been doing this for about a year. Tai Chi pays very precise attention to the smallest details, in this case, moving the energy exactly to the fingertips, not halfway there, not an inch beyond.

So, I was very aware of my fingertips during that time. I tried shifting into my right little finger, trying to move those muscles. I couldn't. I focused on my left little finger, trying to stir some movement. It didn't work. I couldn't reconnect with my body.

There was a feeling of sitting up. My body didn't move, but my spirit, my energy sat up. Again, it was one of those jolts, like seeing the earth. I couldn't make contact with my body, and there was a moment of panic. That's when it dawned on me that there was no life in my body.

Suddenly, I realized that there was somebody else in the house. My other roommate, the medical doctor, was sound asleep in his bedroom. He had come home while I was still sleeping. At that point, I don't even think he knew that I was sick, and he certainly didn't know that I was in any sort of crisis.

I tried to contact him. It was as if I could hear my voice, although my lips weren't moving and I certainly wasn't physically able to call out. It was more like telepathy.

He stirred in his sleep. I called again, and he woke up. But he didn't know what had awakened him. The third time I called, he heard me, but was confused by it.

He got up out of a deep sleep, walked down the hall into the bathroom where the light was on, and found me collapsed on the floor. This is the hard part to describe, but I knew everything he was thinking. I was feeling his thoughts, and I could speak to him.

"Look, you've got to do something quick. I can't get back into my body." I could see that he was bewildered. I told him, "Don't think about this, but go get some big towels and put cold water on my body. Touch my body."

As a physician, this wasn't what he wanted to do. But that's what I was telling him to do, and at that moment I had more impact than his own training. He walked down the hall and turned the corner, well out of sight of the bathroom, and opened up the cupboard. He grabbed the small washcloths, like you'd put on your forehead. I said, "No, no, no! Big towels! Get the big ones!"

At that instant the peculiarity of the situation hit him. He stepped over and looked. I was lying face down on the floor in the other room, and still I was telling him to get the big towels. He went absolutely numb for a moment. He told me later that was when he realized that my voice wasn't coming to him, but it was as if I was talking directly into his mind. "We don't have time to talk about this. Get those towels! Get back in there!"

He grabbed the big towels, wet them down, rolled

me over onto my back, and put these cold towels on my body. I said "Keep touching me!" He was really shaky, and I kept talking to calm him down. "Touch me! Touch me! Touch me! Keep touching my body!"

At the same time, he was checking for vital signs, and not finding any. He realized that I had been gone for some time, probably around ten minutes. I was reading his mind, as he was thinking, "This guy's been dead for a while. I need to call an ambulance." I kept saying, "Don't take your hands off of me!"

Now this doctor had been our friend for years, and knew both Joe and me well. He held our practice in great respect, and I'm sure that influenced his actions at that moment. He was so torn between his medical training, which would have had him on the phone for an ambulance immediately, and staying with exactly what was occurring before him. He was so thrown by seeing my dead body and still hearing my voice, that he absolutely did not know what to do.

He kept touching me, as I talked to him. Up until then I was almost in his body. My experience was almost of looking through his eyes, reading his mind, and telling him what to do.

Suddenly, I was above him, looking down at my own face. I could see my chest and head, unmoving, not breathing. Suddenly, I found myself drifting away, just gently drifting away. I thought, "I'm not going to make it." There was no trauma at all in that realization. It was simply, "It's not going to happen."

And then, boom! Just like that, with no transition, I was down inside my body, looking out of my eyes at my friend kneeling above me. I had the sensation of flickering in my body. He knew when it happened; he felt it happen. He was startled, and I said, "Yes, I'm in my body; I'm in my body now." Telepathically, I was still able to communicate with him.

He kept checking, but even then there were no signs of life at all. Although I was in my body, looking out through my eyes, there was no pulse or breathing. I began to be aware of time, by seeing his movements and feeling his thoughts. He was like a clock for me. About half a minute passed.

Suddenly hot lava poured into every inch of my body. Each and every one of my cells individually exploded. When I came back to life, it was like my entire body was a super nova, a sun bursting in some distant galaxy. It didn't register as pain, but as the most intensely ecstatic physical sensation I'd ever felt. I went literally from my worst moment, being more ill than I could imagine, to the most wonderful moment, erupting back into life, in the space of perhaps ten minutes.

I started to laugh. I was weak, but a soft laughter spilled out of me. All the euphoric energy of life was tingling throughout every inch of my body, and I was absolutely loving it.

I lay there. I told the doctor not to take his hands off of me yet. I still couldn't speak; I was too weak to move. But I could still hear his thoughts, and talk to him, just as I had been the whole time. This went on for several more minutes.

Joe came home, and I've never in my life been happier to see him. He walked in, and the doctor bolted out of the room, saying, "Thank God you're here! This is more than I can handle." I'd kept him there, and at last he could escape to gather his wits about him and to call an ambulance, which he'd wanted to do from the start.

My friend, and he was very dearly my friend, squatted down on the floor next to me. He didn't even look directly at me. What he was doing was sensing me, tuning in to how I was feeling, what I was experiencing. He quietly asked me what I wanted to do. He didn't assume anything. He just said, "Do you want an ambulance? It feels like you're just barely here."

I've never been given so much respect in my whole life. In that moment I really felt his devotion, because he didn't want to impose any scenario on me. He simply asked me what I wanted to do.

I said, "Don't let him call the ambulance. You'll have to forgive me if I die on your bathroom floor, but this is too important to be disturbed right now." I didn't want that hassle, the panic, the rigmarole of the medical profession to interrupt this incredible process. I just wanted to be left alone right then. Whether I lived or died was not the important thing to me. I felt like something so momentous had just occurred, I didn't want to distract myself from fully absorbing the wonder of that experience.

The doctor held Joe in such high regard, that he actually listened to him, and didn't call the ambulance. But he was totally pulled apart, because this violated all his medical training. I am to this day grateful that his open hearted humanity was actually stronger than all his background as a medical doctor.

After another twenty or thirty minutes, they picked me up and put me in bed, where I stayed for several more days. They monitored me, although no more crises occurred.

This deep encounter with silence, called by some a near death experience, began a process that continues to this day. A door was opened for me, which created a very different direction in my life. Since then I have focused my internal awareness on maintaining that silence, a central place that exists in every moment of my life. Externally, I focused my awareness on creating the techniques and language to share this silence.

Seven

It took me years to recover. Days and weeks would roll by, where I was too weak to lift my head, where crawling to the bathroom took a concerted effort. I was instantly an old man, with barely the strength to keep breathing and sleeping.

I was so used to my physical strength and virility, I didn't even know who this person was, this invalid who could do almost nothing. Where was the person who used to jump out of airplanes, ride in the rodeos, go scuba diving, and loved romantic adventures of every kind? Where had that person gone?

This half alive state was much worse than dying. My death experience had been a fascinating adventure, full of rich sensations. This was intolerable.

Lying there, I felt waves of anger and frustration, rising out of my inert body.

I had practiced working with anger for the past several years, as a part of the emotional cleansing that takes place in Tai Chi. This gave me an opportunity to breathe in the belly, and direct the energy downward in my body, letting go and releasing the energy physically. I wanted to see what effect that would have on my emotions.

Well, at first it took me two and a half days after an incident of anger to even remember to try that. I hadn't been actively angry that entire time, of course, but still some remnants of the feeling lingered in the back of my mind, and in my dreams. The process of letting go seemed to clear it up.

Soon, it took me only a few hours to remember to let go. Slowly, I trained myself to shorten that span of time between anger and awareness. Eventually, I learned to watch myself as I was in the midst of my emotions.

What I discovered was that anger and awareness could not coexist. It was one or the other. Awareness simply transforms negative emotions.

Then, I began to notice my tendency toward anger even before it arose, before any outside trigger gave it an excuse to erupt. I could feel, even before I got out of bed in the morning, that I had an angry inclination on that particular day. I observed the rhythms that shaped my emotional life, like recurrent weather patterns. This insight gave me some degree of freedom. With this perspective, my own emotions could no longer sneak up on me.

In my infirmity, I was trapped in a situation I couldn't escape. I couldn't improve my condition, or distract myself in any way. I felt completely helpless. There was such anger and frustration, far more devastating than anything I had felt before.

I needed every bit of my Tai Chi training, especially the internal meditations, to survive and to cope with my illness. The only exercise I could do during this period was that of circulating the energy of my breath through my body. I could do this Tai Chi meditation without moving a muscle. Even when I was too exhausted to read a book, I could practice this awareness training exercise, which I did for hours on end.

What it taught me was simply incredible. I had just as much energy as I did in my rambunctious youth. It had shifted to the inside, where it wasn't visible. I could be too weak to hold my eyes open, and still be spiritually very potent.

It was like learning to see in the dark. When I first looked inward, I couldn't see anything at all, like I'd come in from the bright glare into a pitch black room. Slowly, slowly, I was becoming accustomed to seeing in that twilight, and I was starting to discern the dimensions of my own energy.

It's the strangest thing. It's like we each have a super nova burning inside of us, but we're too distracted to notice it because we happen to be watching television. The most trivial thing in the outside world is enough to distract us.

The death experience and the long, long recovery period put my awareness training into fast-forward.

I learned more in a few years than I would have in decades, even practicing Tai Chi four hours a day. The illness became my teacher, forcing me to be still long enough to really see what it is that Tai Chi is aiming toward.

Like most people, I had feared getting old. The idea of losing my vitality, of becoming helpless, was more of an indignity than death itself.

Now I could see that it was not aging that I had to fear, but unawareness. I could actually experience that my life was even more vital, more potent now than it had ever been. Externally, I was too weak to move, but a furnace was lit inside of me. Without awareness training, this would have been a torture. With it, the illness became a gift.

This time of convalescence gave me an opportunity to understand my own strong emotions. Rather than affixing a specific cause in the outside world to explain the way I felt, I realized that what I was experiencing was my own energy. I opened up the space to feel a much broader range of my own feelings.

What I had experienced as an undercurrent of anger turned out to be sadness. That grief had a lot to do with the extermination of the Native Americans, and of nature itself, in this country. The desecration of this beautiful and sacred environment left these people nothing to do but to be jailed on reservations, to go into hiding, as my family had done, or simply to die from loss of heart. I was unable to shake the feeling that it was all happening to me! Tears came up over and over again, and for years I lived that sorrow. Unexplainable memories surfaced, and I slowly assimilated all the history of my people and this spectacular land.

I realized, if I was willing to go that deeply, I could actually feel what was occurring to the earth. Each of us reflects the whole. The resensitizing that happens in awareness training heals the fragmentation of spirit that underlies the devastation we see around us. By falling into rhythm with the emotional and spiritual heartbeat of nature, the differences that separate us simply disappear. Each of us carries the weight of what is happening to the earth, either consciously or unconsciously. By summoning the courage to feel it overtly, we can participate in the slow process of healing. Nature has an incredible capacity to recover and rejuvenate, given the opportunity.

As I spent these long days and weeks in bed, too weak to do anything, I continued to observe my own internal processes. One thing I had to come to terms with was the constant state of dissatisfaction that had shaped my life.

I had always felt somehow incomplete, like there was still something else that needed to happen. Despite moments of satiety, when I could relax, or moments of exhaustion, when I'd had enough, I continued to feel dissatisfied. This had led me to seek new and interesting experiences, but they only satisfied me temporarily.

At the very center of my near-death experience, there was an opening into that space where the dissatisfaction ceased. It's not accurate to say that I became satisfied, because that implies that something came to fulfill a need I had, like food when I'm hungry. Instead, the dissatisfaction simply evaporated.

My first taste of awareness, those moments of sheer perfection when existence could not possibly be better, happened out in nature. Later, such glimpses of ecstasy came through sex. Tai Chi gave me a practical method to approach such a state. But it was death and my long convalescence that allowed me the deepest contact with grace, with the power of life itself.

One particular memory surfaced during this time of convalescence.

Joe and I had been driving through town one evening, several years before. He was telling me stories of his life, the people he'd known, the ones that had most affected him. I heard the sorrow in his voice as he described a friend he'd very much respected, who had disappeared from his life by becoming a disciple to a master, and gone away to some foreign land.

That moment is etched permanently in my memory. I saw the flicker of streetlights, passing by in the dark sky, reflected in the asphalt. I was so deeply touched by the mention of a disciple, a master, even though I had never encountered the idea before. I had no concept of what it meant. My young mind, full of knowledge, knew absolutely nothing about that possibility. The streetlights flashed by like the passing of time. I felt myself existing in many lives, throughout time.

The very possibility of such a decision, such a commitment, was beyond anything I had ever imagined. I had literally never heard of anyone even contemplating such a radical departure from normal life. At the same time I felt Joe's sense of loss, as if his friend had disappeared into a realm so strange as to be completely inaccessible.

Although it had a distinct impact on me, at the time I had no context for this occurrence. This was a germinal idea, a seed that was all too easy to overlook because it had no setting, no place alongside anything else in my life.

This seemingly endless time of convalescence allowed a deepening within me. As I reexamined this memory, I began to value and to nurture that seed.

My illness put me into touch with a reality even more essential than the physical world. In a way it was like sensory deprivation, leading me inwards. Somehow, that made the physical world itself even more precious. Each sunrise became joyous, each twilight, something to be celebrated. The touch of the air moving across my skin felt like a sensuous caress.

I used to feel like one person among all the billions on this small planet, having good days and bad days, hoping to create my ideal life, hoping for happiness.

Now I felt like a person under the sky, touched by heaven, supported by the earth. Blessings were constantly flowing down, and the nourishment of the earth was constantly uprising. The universe was a living, caring place. It wasn't neutral. This incredible richness was showering down on me at every moment, without exception. This totally neutralized the ambitions and desires that used to motivate me. It seemed impossible that things could be better than this. Just the fact of being alive was more than enough.

Eight

There are Tai Chi meditation practices that are done during sleep, bringing awareness to the act of dreaming. One definitive dream stands out in my mind from the period immediately after my death experience.

Years before the death experience, I had been given the name, White Wolf during a vision quest in the desert, with two Native American elders, men of great understanding. I never used that name, and almost no one knew about it. I kept it to myself, part of my own buried treasure, my essence.

Six days after the death experience, I had a dream that crystallized the new priorities of my life. I dreamed of galloping through a wilderness, clutching the mane of my mount, delighted by the world surrounding me. It was intact, a living, breathing wilderness that expanded well beyond all the horizons. We rode to the crest of a hill, where I slid off and gazed at the unmarred lands stretching out beneath me. I felt the wind in my face, and just reveled in the beauty, the sensuality of that moment.

When I turned back to remount, I noticed that it was not a horse, it was a huge white wolf that I'd been riding! Joyfully, I ran up and threw my arms around its neck, melting into the warmth of its soft white fur.

Upon waking from that dream, I realized that I was going to remain with that which had been called 'White Wolf.' That essence, which I had buried deeply within me, I was no longer willing to hide. White Wolf was a name for that joy, that way of being, that flavor of silence. I was no longer willing to compromise. My decisions would be made on whether it felt right in that place of silence. This inner peace was no longer going to be a hidden gem buried deep within me. But rather like a seed that has germinated, silence began to move outward into every aspect of my life.

We live in a world where nature is disappearing as a living entity. We have pieces of it that still live; the trees and the animals still live in some places. But the organic reality of nature as an unbroken whole that surrounds the earth is dissolving into the world of people. As men, as women, we are part of nature as well, but we suffer from our lack of daily contact with nature, from its wisdom.

Tai Chi, which the natural world gave me the eyes to see, steadily directs us inward. The sensitivity honed by the wilderness gave me a glimpse of its potential, let me know to follow that path. Tai Chi unfolds the nature within us.

We are the flowering of nature. Unfolding that center through this moving meditation reveals the potential of every human being, showing the grandeur within each of us.

It was impossible to communicate with anyone I knew at the depth I was now experiencing. During my illness, the I Ching was my friend. The I Ching is an oracle, a book of wisdom to use as a resource for creating deep introspection. Whenever I would meditate over very important issues and still couldn't come to any conclusion, the I Ching was always there to offer guidance. I have found it to be completely accurate throughout my life. It would not only confirm my intuition, but guide me to deeper insights. Behind all the words I could always sense the heartbeat of silence.

If I tried to consult it superficially, I was lost. But it always seemed to speak to these subterranean depths. That was the only level at which it spoke directly.

About a week after the death experience, and just after I had the White Wolf dream, I mustered enough strength to consult the I Ching. I received "Return-The Turning Point," which read:

"The hexagram counsels turning away from the confusion of external things, turning back to one's inner light. There, in the depths of the soul, one sees the Divine, the One. It is indeed only germinal, no more than a beginning, a potentiality, but as such clearly to be distinguished from all objects..."

The phrase, 'clearly to be distinguished from all objects' kept reverberating within me. That expressed something essential about what occurred during those ten minutes of death, before I reentered my life.

It was not an object, not an experience, not an emotion, not a thought, and not a conclusion. None of these were important. It was pure emptiness, the field of consciousness itself, without an object. That was what had been so incredibly wonderful in the core of my death experience.

This death encounter changed the way I experienced life in a fundamental way. Before, I had felt a definite schism between three distinctly different arenas in my life. The sphere of people, the natural wilderness, and the realm of dreams were three distinctly different worlds, which had almost nothing in common.

I had very enthusiastically given myself up to the pull of nature, where the concerns were of a very practical sort. Alertness and clarity were vital, sometimes lifesaving, but the thinking process was secondary.

Mind was irrelevant, what was required was decisive swift action.

In the domain of human interaction, being awake was actually an impediment. You had to play the game a certain way, and it was better not to see that the game itself was absurd. I enjoyed people, but often felt somewhat confined, like my energy couldn't come fully out. If I wasn't careful I would unwittingly stumble into these social booby traps, these arbitrary cultural anomalies. Missteps taken out of pure innocence created misunderstandings, so I felt restrained in that arena.

Dreams were occasionally insightful, but they were erratic, appearing on a whim of their own. While interesting, dreams were too unreliable to deal with consistently. Though they sometimes had a major impact, it was nothing I could call forth.

Before my death experience, emptiness had been only glimpsed during my days of solitude in the wilderness. That's exactly what was out of kilter in my life up to this point. Silence had only been a certain part of one of these three worlds, a fragment. It never had its rightful place.

Now I understood that void to be a domain of its own, a fourth world that was the root, the core out of which the other worlds grew.

Emptiness was the absolute center, the essential source. Silence was the sound I heard in the wind, the sound I heard when my mouth opened, the heartbeat I felt in other people.

This world of silence became much stronger for me. With that as the hub of the wheel, the other three worlds fell into place much more easily. They seemed to suddenly make sense, and I understood that I could access silence through people, or through dreams, as well as through nature.

The three worlds diminished in importance, and emptiness, which had been just a distant glimmer in the sky, became all important. That centering changed the entire direction of my life. In this way my priorities, my vision shifted radically with my death experience.

By taking that sense of freedom and wholeness back into the world of people, human interactions began to change for me. I didn't have to go on hold, and I could express much more than I had realized. People and nature were not, after all, so different.

My dreaming went through a radical transformation. I learned to become aware in the midst of dreaming. If the mind was simply churning, processing unfinished business, the dream would evaporate. But if it contained real information, it would become more colorful, focused, and alive. Awareness was nourished by these vivid dreams, which again gave access to the realm beyond dreaming, where the imagery of dreams is not necessary. Without the visual or the verbal, emptiness speaks directly, and silence is its voice.

Tai Chi had been pointing in this direction for years. It created an opportunity, slowly and with infinite patience, for an experience of silence.

Tai Chi, and the I Ching which is its base, were the only bridges I had known between the worlds that had once seemed so separate. Tai Chi walked well in the world of people. It teaches a practical way to maintain your space without over pushing or collapsing, while still allowing for a full exchange of energy. Because it is so soft in approach, it provokes relaxation rather than aggression.

It is a nature based system, employing the imagery of water flowing downward, letting go, flowing around obstacles, as a model for human interaction. The sequence is rooted in a keen observation of nature, derived from the movements of animals... 'Two Birds Flying,' 'Crane Cools His Wings,' and 'Snake Spits Out His Tongue.' The integration of these separate spheres of my life was begun by Tai Chi. The death experience made the whole subtle process much more apparent. I had a powerful, instantaneous experience of the silence that Tai Chi is aiming toward. The long convalescence forced me to stay with that awareness, rather than being distracted again by the external world.

All my life I've loved adventures, physical, psychological and emotional, adventures of all kinds. There used to be a need for an adrenalin rush to give my life a good shake, to freshen things up, so the routines were tolerable for awhile. Then there would be a settling back to normality, which was composed of patterns that always seemed arbitrary to me. Things were more or less the same after the excitement had dropped away.

As silence grew, adventure itself began to change. Emptiness created new patterns, and things began to fall into an organic, unplanned whole, a shape that seemed naturally to fit. I didn't feel compelled to climb every mountain, to ride every horse, to dance with every woman who came along. I didn't need physical challenges to get my endorphins racing or to push my endurance to the limit in order to relieve the boredom. In fact, boredom wasn't experienced anymore.

Much more subtle experiences, listening to the birds, watching the sunrise, just breathing and being alive seemed like adventures to me now. It used to be that something radically different had to occur in order to satisfy me. After returning from death, the smallest occurrences could have the same dynamic impact.

The big adventures were still to happen in my life, travelling to different parts of the world, exploring other cultures. In fact, bigger surprises than I had ever imagined were in store. But there was no need for me to create them, they simply happened on their own.

One such experience occurred about six months after we opened the cafe. My cousin was in a train wreck and had slipped into a coma. My first thought was to go there, but my mother said that the family was being taken care of, and there was enough support for everyone. She felt it was best for me to wait.

He was in that coma for twenty eight days, which seemed like forever. During that time, I called frequently to check his status. But I also spent time every day becoming very still and quiet, to see if I could feel what his internal process might be like. Three times I felt like I tuned in and actually had long conversations with him.

My cousin eventually recovered, and it was two years later that we spent a stretch of time together at my grandmother's house. We were eating a plateful of her delicious fried peach pies, when I asked my cousin whether he remembered anything from that month he was in a coma.

He looked down and became really quiet. I hoped I hadn't overstepped my bounds.

"It's interesting you asked," he said glancing up. "The only thing I remember is having three conversations with you." He then went on to relate those conversations in detail, just as I'd experienced them.

Another of these experiences occurred after my own near-death. My grandmother went into a coma during surgery at a hospital. By this time, I was already on the Big Island of Hawai'i. My father called and asked me to come home, saying that she might die at any time.

I went into my room to pack a suitcase. I paused, and sat down in the chair where I always wrote and played my flute. I sat looking out the big picture window at the trees and sky, with the clouds rolling in off the ocean, carrying a little bit of rain.

I had a vision of my grandmother and myself on the front porch of a house I'd never seen. We were looking at each other, smiling, and then we turned and looked at the doorway. I reached down to turn the handle, but seemed to be clumsy, like I was struggling to open it. My grandmother said, "We don't have much time." I realized that she was about to die. Suddenly I understood that if I didn't open this door for her, I would never see her alive again. With that, I completely focused my attention on opening that door. She passed through the entryway, and I followed her inside. That ended the vision.

I sat quietly for another twenty minutes. It became perfectly clear to me that I was not going back to Texas. I sat there and wrote my grandmother a long letter, expressing the joy of life, the adventure of death, and the pleasure of our relationship. I wrote for a couple of hours.

My dad could not understand why I was not catching the next plane back home. But I mailed that letter, and my grandmother came out of her coma the same day my letter arrived. My aunt read her the letter that morning, and she asked to hear it everyday thereafter, during her convalescence. My grandmother went on to live another fifteen years after that incident.

My family are not New Age people. Far from it. My cousin bales hay for a living out in East Texas, and my grandmother headed a household that encompassed four generations. But somehow, during those interludes between life and death, we were able to make contact.

道

I'll never forget the impact of the Big Island of Hawai'i when I first arrived. A friend of mine had been planning a trip, and about twenty hours before he left, I decided to go with him. So I had no time to form any expectations about the place.

We landed in Hilo. Even in town, the human activity was dwarfed by the scale of nature. Massive banyan trees looked like something out of a kid's fairy tale. Stately African tulip trees and Royal Poinsiannas blazed with color, exploding into the sky. Philodendrons with leaves three feet across sprouted sensual looking white blossoms in a tropical profusion. I had never seen such a lush palette of greens and blues.

The turquoise of the bay stretched out into the deeper blue of the Pacific, which reached into the sky of the eastern horizon. To the west, the snowy peak of Mauna Kea seemed near enough to touch.

Out of nowhere, the sky just spilled open into a hearty downpour. Ten minutes later, the sun was shining again, casting rainbows across the mountain slopes.

The second day, we drove to the volcano, where lava was flowing steadily toward the ocean. A finger of molten earth about twenty feet high and thirty feet wide inched its way slowly to the sea. It was the crumbly textured lava called a'a. Pieces of the flow were constantly dropping off, revealing the glowing red interior. The earth was alive in this place.

This felt like the right setting for my body and spirit to be rejuvenated. I didn't know about the details of my life, how I would earn a living, what work I would do. But this primal, thriving garden seemed like the right place for me to come back to life. So I decided to stay. Soon Joe came to the island as well, and we spent much of the next decade living close by each other and studying Tai Chi together.

The Big Island of Hawai'i, where I've lived for most of the past nineteen years, has been the lovely setting for my own growth. There was a Native Hawaiian kahuna, or 'keeper of the secret,' a woman named Morrnah Simeona, who seemed to live in a world others rarely even thought about. She understood the interface between the spirit world and this reality, and specialized in cleansings enacted through that invisible realm. Morrnah was chosen as a kahuna lapa'au, or healer, as a young child, and received the gift of healing at the age of three.

My time with Morrnah felt like sitting by the river. Side by side, we sat, observing that river of light, asking a few questions, confirming that we were seeing the same things. She had much more experience sitting by this river than I.

I used to get up early in the morning to do my Tai Chi practice, then wait until a decent hour, 5:30 or so, to see if Morrnah was awake. I'd stand outside where she would catch sight of me. This gave her the option of either ignoring me, in which case I'd leave immediately, or giving a slight nod, signaling that it was all right for me to come in and sit with her.

Years later, the State of Hawai'i recognized Morrnah as a living treasure. I was always delighted that not only those of us who were interested in such things, but the state as a whole, recognized someone of her stature and insight.

Morrnah looked like she could be your grandmother, or your elementary school teacher. She had both sweetness and sternness, combined with a very powerful personal presence. She taught me Ho'Oponopono, the Hawaiian technique for stripping away the energy body, cleansing and revitalizing it, and putting it back in place.

You could see the effects of this practice in a crowd. Everyone was interested in her, but none would get too close. She had a force field around her that extended about three feet, and no one would violate that space.

One day, there were dozens of people around. I listened for about two hours as she answered questions, and finally decided to ask one of my own.

"I feel like I'm right on the cusp of a huge change, like a very important teacher or teaching is coming into my life," I began.

Morrnah stopped me. "I know exactly what you're talking about. You may feel that it's me," she paused. "I acknowledge how you feel about me. I feel the same way toward you. But I am not that teacher. Your instincts are right, and you'll just have to wait. The one who is coming into your life can give you so much more than I can. I am not your master, but your master is coming." ...

Meditation Center

Natural Advantage was co-founded by Tom Grunden and Kathy Mason with a long-term goal of creating a permanent meditation center on the Big Island of Hawai'i. A percentage of the proceeds from this book is committed to that goal.

Any and all donations will be gratefully accepted. If you would like to contribute, please send to:

Natural Advantage
69-1010 Keana Pl., C-101
Kamuela, HI 96743

Also Offered By Natural Advantage

Tom Grunden is an internationally known consultant, speaker, and teacher. He is available for workshops, seminars and private consultation on the following:

> Awareness Training • Intuition • Listening
> Stress Management • Relaxation
> Meditation – Moving, Dancing, Sitting
> Tai Chi • Chi Kung • Push-hands
> Death & Dieing Workshops
> I Ching

Also Available:

I Ching	Audio cassette tape of Tom Grunden's methods for consulting and interpreting the I Ching	$11

Tai Chi Meditation $11
Audio cassette tape for internal practice of Tai Chi
Side A 8 stretches – easy for anyone to follow
Side B Circulation of the energy of the breath through the body (easy to follow tape for internal Tai Chi practice without the movements.) Used while lying down. Effective for active or physically challenged persons.

Tai Chi Chuan	Video Tape, Yang Style Long Form, First 18 movements 52 Minutes (Very clear instruction)	$20
Chi Kung	Audio cassette tape	$11

Certification Programs:

> Chi Kung • Tai Chi Chih • Tai Chih Chuan

Natural Advantage, 69-1010 Keana Pl., C-101, Kamuela, HI 96743

1-800-293-2911

About the Author

Tom Grunden holds dual degrees in psychology and engineering physics from the University of Texas where he graduated magna cum laude. He has owned several successful businesses and is an internationally known consultant, speaker, and teacher of stress management through a broad spectrum of relaxation techniques.

Tom has been teaching Tai Chi and Chi Kung for 24 years, eight of them at the Hyatt and Hilton hotels on the Big Island of Hawai'i. He has introduced these moving meditations to over 45,000 people, from the physically challenged to olympic athletes as well as to individuals and corporations from around the world. His presentations are so lively and enjoyable that the hotels have received over 600 letters from guests expressing appreciation for their life-enhancing experiences with him.

Tom's life has been strongly influenced by an undercurrent of his Native American heritage and the study of all the religions of the world. He also studied Ho 'Oponopono, in depth, with Hawai'i's state treasure of healing, Kahuna Lapa'au Morrnah Simeona and she forecasted his meeting with a living master, the story he tells in his next book. The I Ching, The Ancient Book of Wisdom, has been Tom's constant companion for 25 years and his completed book on this subject will be published soon.